Brilliant Br

Chapter 1: Reading by Dots .... page 2

Chapter 2: Paris .... page 6

Chapter 3: Louis... page 11

Chapter 4: The Chase .... page 18

Chapter 5: Louis's Invention .... page 25

Written by Adam and Charlotte Guillain

Chapter 1: Reading by Dots

It was the summer holidays and Asha's dad had taken Finn and Rav to the museum for the day.

"What's that girl doing?" whispered Rav as he spotted a girl putting her hand over one of the signs.

They walked over to the girl. She was picking up a clay pot.

"Are you allowed to touch that?" Finn asked her.

The girl smiled and put the pot down.

"It's okay," she said, running her fingers over a bowl. "This area is especially for people like me."

Rav frowned. "What do you mean?"

"I'm blind," she explained. "So I need to use my hands to understand what things look like." She was quiet as she ran her finger over another sign.

"It says these things are hundreds of years old," she told them.

Finn looked at the sign but all he could see were dots.

"It's Braille," the girl explained. "Instead of looking at letters, I use these dots to read."

As the girl moved on, Finn ran his fingers over the Braille. At once, the lights started flickering.

"We're going back in time!" yelled Rav as they whirled away.

Chapter 2: Paris

When they stopped moving, Rav and Finn were standing in a street. A horse and carriage rattled past and people in old-fashioned clothes hurried by.

"Where are we?" asked Rav, gazing around.

Finn looked up at a street sign. "That looks like French!" he said.

A cart trundled past the boys and they gasped.

"Wow, Paris!" said Rav. "I've always wanted to come here. Let's explore!"

They set off down the street but a rumble of thunder made them stop. Torrential rain began to pour down and everyone began running for shelter.

"Quick!" shouted Finn.

The door of a nearby building was open and the boys darted inside. They stood in the entrance and stared at the rain splashing in the street.

"Looks like we're stuck in here for a while," sighed Finn.

We're still getting wet. Let's go inside.

"It looks like a classroom," whispered Rav, staring at all the children sitting at desks.

"They're reading books with their fingers, like the girl in the museum!" said Finn, and he opened one of the books at an empty desk. "I think this must be a school for blind children."

Finn looked more closely at the book's pages. They were covered in large raised letters, not dots.

"Oh, it's not Braille," he said, feeling disappointed.

"It looks as if it takes a long time to finish a story that way," said Rav, watching the children's fingers moving very slowly.

Chapter 3: Louis

"Who are you?" said a boy behind them. "I don't recognise your voices."

Rav and Finn spun around.

"This is Finn," said Rav, "and I'm Rav."

"I'm Louis," said the boy.

"What are you doing?" asked Finn. Louis was using a tool to make raised dots in a piece of thick paper.

"I'm fed up with trying to read the books the school has given us," said Louis. "I'm trying to invent a new type of writing for blind people." Louis held up his sheet of paper. "You run your finger over the dots and you can read much more quickly," he said.

Finn opened his mouth in amazement and stared at Rav. He was about to speak when a loud, deep voice bellowed, "Louis Braille! What are you doing?"

A teacher came striding towards them. Rav and Finn quickly ducked down and hid under the desk.

"I'm tired of seeing you waste your time, boy," the teacher shouted. "Put this rubbish away and go and read a book with all the other students."

"But …" Louis started to say, but the teacher cut him off and stomped away.

Louis sighed and put his papers on the windowsill.

"It's no good," he told Rav and Finn. "Nobody here believes my idea will work. Perhaps I should just give up."

He walked across the room and sat down with one of the huge books, his head hanging.

Rav nudged Finn. "Did you hear what the teacher called him? Louis *Braille*! He must be the inventor of Braille," he whispered.

Finn's eyes widened. "We can't let him give up then!" he said. "He has no idea how important his invention is!"

A movement at the window made Rav and Finn turn. A gust of wind rustled the sheets of paper Louis had left. Rav ran across to the window just in time to see the paper fly up in the air and out into the street. "Oh no!" he gasped.

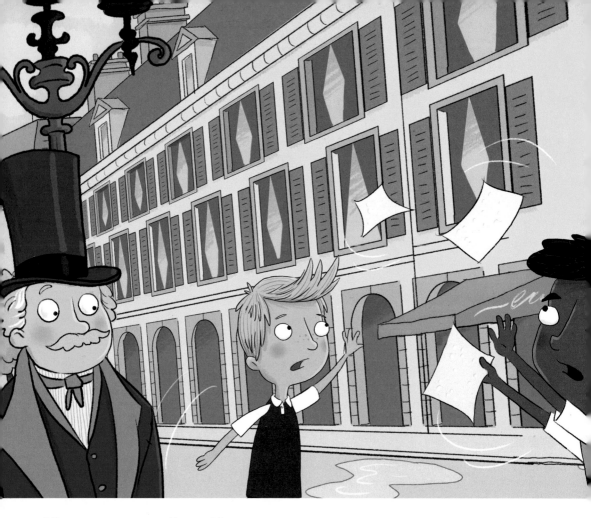

Chapter 4: The Chase

Finn and Rav glanced at Louis, who was bent unhappily over a book.

"Come on!" hissed Finn and they sprinted from the room and out into the street. It had stopped raining but the sheets of paper were fluttering towards a huge puddle.

"Quickly!" yelled Rav.

They skidded to a halt in front of the puddle and leaped in the air to catch the pages.

"Have we got them all?" called Finn, looking around frantically.

"No!" groaned Rav. "Look!"

The last sheet of paper blew up higher and glided towards a carriage standing in the street.

As the boys watched, a man slammed the carriage door shut.

"The paper's trapped in the door!" cried Finn.

The driver flicked the reins and the horses started to trot off down the street.

"Come on!" shouted Rav, and they began running behind it.

Through the bustling, narrow streets of Paris, the boys sprinted after the carriage. It clattered around a corner and Finn and Rav found themselves running beside a wide river.

"I'm getting tired," puffed Rav, holding his side.

"Keep going!" urged Finn, his eyes fixed on the flapping piece of paper.

Trees appeared at the side of the river and the carriage turned into an elegant park.

"It's stopping," panted Rav in relief.

The carriage door opened and the precious sheet of paper drifted towards the boys.

"Got it!" wheezed Finn as he gripped it tightly between his fingers.

When they had got their breath back, Rav and Finn started walking back to the school.

"This was the name of the street, wasn't it?" said Finn, looking up.

"Yes! Look, there's the school," said Rav.

They ran inside, straight into the path of a very tall, angry-looking man.

"What are you doing in my school?" boomed the man.

"Um, we're here to see Louis Braille," stammered Rav.

"Why? Pupils aren't permitted visitors during lesson time!" shouted the headmaster.

"He needs to show you his invention," said Finn, holding out the sheets of paper.

Chapter 5: Louis's Invention

They followed the headmaster into the classroom where Louis was still hunched over a book.

"Louis Braille!" bellowed the headmaster. "What is this invention of yours these boys are talking about?"

Louis stood up with his mouth open.

"Go on, Louis, tell him," Rav whispered. Louis began to smile and he cleared his throat.

"Do you have a newspaper, sir?" Louis asked the headmaster.

"Yes," said the headmaster, frowning.

Louis pulled the paper-punching tool from his pocket and Rav handed him a sheet of clean paper.

"Please could you read a short article from your newspaper to me slowly?" Louis asked.

As the headmaster started to read, Louis punched the dots very quickly in the paper. When the headmaster had finished reading, Louis grinned and said, "I used my special writing to copy the article you read. I'll read it back to you."

Louis repeated the article word for word, and the headmaster stared at him.

"That's incredible!" cried the headmaster. He picked up the paper and ran his fingers over the dots Louis had punched. "You must tell me more about it," the headmaster went on, putting his hand on Louis's shoulder. Louis beamed and started to explain, just as the lights started to flash.

Rav and Finn were swept back to the museum. Rav held out his hand.

"Look, I've got some rough paper with Louis's Braille writing on it!" he said.

"You can use it for your summer project!" said Finn. "Come on, let's see if we can find any more Braille signs!"

Brilliant Braille

What other things will the Comet Street Kids collect
for their holiday challenge? Read the other books
in this band to find out!

Brilliant Braille

Stop Shouting!

Stranded Panda

A Midsummer Night's Disaster

The Missing Cat

Moonquake

Talk about the story

Answer the questions:

1 Which city did the friends travel to?

2 What language was the street sign in?

3 Can you explain what Braille is?

4 Why was Finn 'feeling disappointed' on page 10?

5 What does the word 'recognise' mean? (page 11)

6 Why did the boys need to take the papers back to the school?

7 Can you describe how Louis demonstrated his invention to the headmaster?

8 Can you think of some other inventions that are helpful to people? Think of something that you use every day.

Can you retell the story in your own words?